BUILDING SKILLS BY EXPLORING MAPS

United States and Canada

Written and Edited by
Alaska Hults

Illustrator: Mapping Specialists
Cover Illustrator: Rick Grayson
Designer: Barbara Peterson
Cover Designer: Barbara Peterson
Art Director: Tom Cochrane
Project Director: Carolea Williams

Table of Contents

Introduction

The wonderful thing about teaching students map skills is that they really want to know how to read maps. To students maps are keys to unknown places. Maps hold the promise of an adventure.

Middle-elementary students understand that maps represent places. However, they do not have much experience making inferences from maps. They assume north is straight up, and they become confused by over-crowed maps. The maps in *United States and Canada* provide an excellent bridge to a much deeper understanding of map reading by eliminating extra details—but not so many that the map loses all context.

As students work with the maps in *United States and Canada*, they will

- explain and use the coordinate grid system of latitude and longitude to determine the absolute locations of places on Earth.

- read and interpret Political maps.

- estimate distances between two places on a map, using a scale of miles, and use cardinal and ordinal directions when referring to relative location.

- know world patterns of resource distribution and utilization.

- use a variety of maps and documents to identify physical and culture features of neighborhoods, cities, states and countries.

- obtain information about a topic using a variety of visual sources such as pictures, symbols, and maps.

You do not have to use the maps in this book in order. Full lessons on each region or city are not provided. Supplement difficult concepts with lessons from your social studies curriculum. Schedule about 20 minutes for each map experience. Invite students to bring in maps they find, and have the class examine them. Have the class find the title, key, scale, compass rose, and lines of latitude and longitude on the map.

Invite students to compare the maps to other maps of the same places. Have them discuss where they see concentrations of settlements. Invite them to place older maps side by side with current maps to observe changes in a region over time. If they spend enough time with the maps and activity sheets, they will better understand the geography of these two countries better. They will also better retain the names and locations of the places they read about or hear about in the news. Conveniently, the skills will also transfer well to a standardized-testing situation.

How to Use This Book

Hitting the Map Standards

Before you have students read and complete the activity page that precedes each map, lay a firm foundation for the activity by having students complete the Evaluate the Map reproducible (page 5). This reproducible will keep students' map skills sharp for test-taking and will better prepare them to think critically as they complete the activity page that accompanies the map. The first few times that you have students evaluate a map, guide them through completing the reproducible. Copy the map to an overhead transparency and display the map so you can point to specific elements of the map during discussion. You may want to use the following tips as you do so.

1. Have students work in pairs the first time they complete the reproducible. More details are identified when two pairs of eyes examine the same map.

2. Have a volunteer read aloud the directions. Emphasize that students should be as complete as possible in their answers. This is especially important for questions 6, 7, and 9.

3. Students may simply copy the title for question 1. For question 2, they should not repeat the information in the title. Have them carefully examine the map and ask the following questions:

   • This map was created by a person. What was the person trying to show or teach in this map?

   • Is there a lot of general information or a little very specific information?

   • Is there anything here that seems out of place? What is it and why do you think the map maker included it?

4. Students may need a thorough review of the map terms before they can complete question 3. Assign colors to each check box, and have students circle or underline parts of the map that correspond to each check box. Invite volunteers to do so on the overhead map.

5. Students will benefit from handling the globe for question 4. Help students find the lines of latitude and longitude. Have them notice the direction abbreviation after each measurement. Have them find North America. Point out that North America is in the northern and western hemispheres. Model how to relate the map to an area on the globe using latitude and longitude. These maps were produced with a variety of projections to minimize distortion, but land closer to the poles will still show some distortion. Point out any discrepancies you see between the flat maps and the globe. Help students picture the edge of the maps as a number line and the intersecting lines of latitude or longitude as points on the number line. Help them estimate the approximate measurement of the points at each corner.

6. For question 5, model how to use a ruler to understand the scale. The activity sheets will provide more practice with using the scale to find actual distances. If students struggle with the scale, have them use the ruler to add additional hatch marks to the scale.

7. For questions 6, 7, and 8 students may simply look at the map and copy the appropriate titles for each item. Question 8 will not always have a visibly obvious answer. Accept all reasonable estimates.

8. Question 9 is fairly self-explanatory. You may invite students to pick four symbols to describe if the key is very detailed and time is short.

Evaluate the Map

Use the map to answer the questions.

1. What is the title of the map?_____

2. What does the map aim to convey?_____

3. Check the box. This map . . .

   ❑ shows political boundaries.

   ❑ shows land and water features.

   ❑ has a key.

   ❑ has a scale.

   ❑ includes a compass rose.

   ❑ has grid lines.

   ❑ has lines of latitude and longitude.

   ❑ shows individual towns or cities.

   ❑ includes information specific to the people who live there such as the kinds of business conducted, level of education, or locations of conflict.

4. Use what you know about latitude and longitude to estimate the following:
   This map spans from _____ to _____ latitude and from _____ to _____ longitude.

5. Align the zero on a ruler with the edge of the scale. Describe the scale in terms of inches and miles or centimeters and kilometers (e.g., The scale is 500 miles for each 1.5 inches.) _____
   _____
   _____

6. List some of the land features that are labeled on the map.

7. List any water features that are labeled on the map.

8. Which body of water appears to cover the greatest area? _____

9. Describe the key. What symbols are shown? How do they help you understand the information on the map? _____
   _____
   _____
   _____

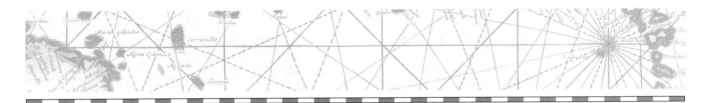

Using the Activity Pages

Each of the activity pages contains a short section with enough information about the place featured on the map for students to put what they see in context. Knowing more about the history or people of a location also provides them with mental hooks that help them remember what they see.

The pages contain either 10 questions to which students will respond, or six multiple-choice questions similar to those found on standardized tests. These ten questions include those that address coordinates in latitude and longitude, scale, direction relative to a location, reading the key, and relating the map to the background information provided on each page.

Latitude and Longitude

The challenge at this level is that the students' ability to read the map is strong enough that they would rather hunt for a location than use latitude and longitude to find it. So, each activity page has at least two questions that require students to use this skill. They are asked to find a location using given coordinates. Then, they are asked to estimate the coordinates of a given location. The answer key provides a possible response. You will need to determine the skill level of your students and the scale of the map to decide the acceptable margin of error. Students with a great deal of map experience may be asked to be more exact than students who are just learning. The skill of estimating map coordinates is actually fairly complex—students must be able to determine the difference between the two nearest lines (e.g., Are there five degrees between lines? Ten? Fifteen?) and then they must divide the space between those lines into equal areas to find, essentially, each degree between the lines. Finally, if the scale is fairly large, they may need to estimate the distance between each degree. In this book, most coordinates were rounded to the nearest degree. There are a few exceptions where it was rounded to the nearest half degree.

Scale

Although this is a difficult concept for students, once they grasp it they want to measure everything. As with latitude and longitude, provide students new to the skill with a greater margin of error. All of the distances on this map were estimated using one of the two following methods and are not intended to replace any figures you might see listed in a detailed reference of the cities.

Method One—Give each student a blank index card. Have students align the top left corner of the card with the left edge of the scale. Have them use a pencil to copy the hatch marks of the scale and their labels onto the top edge of the card. Have them move the card so that the last hatch mark aligns with the first mark of the scale and extend the scale on their card to double its length. Students should calculate the new distances and add those to their scale. If hatch marks are more than 1/4" apart, have them use a ruler to divide the area between hatch marks into smaller equal sections. Have them calculate the value of each of the new hatch marks and add that to their scale. This will facilitate more accurate estimates of distance. Then, have them measure distance by aligning the left edge of the card with the center of the first point and then rotating the card until the edge of it passes through the center of the second point. Students should then use the scale on the

The Activity Pages

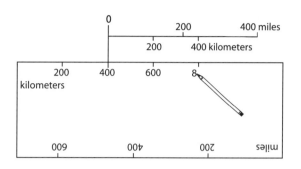

edge of the card to estimate the distance. This is an easy and effective way to measure more than one location. Extend the activity by having students copy miles onto one edge of the card and kilometers onto the other.

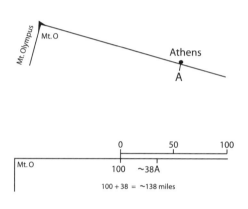

Method Two—Give students a blank index card. Have students align the left corner of the card with the center of the first point. Have them rotate the card until the edge of the card passes through the center of the second point. Then, have them mark the location of the second place on the edge of the card. Finally, have them align the edge of the card with the scale and compare to find the distance. If the distance exceeds the length of the scale on the map, have them make a small mark to show the end of the scale, move that mark back to zero, and measure the remaining distance. Then, students add the two distances together to find the total distance. This is an easy and effective way to measure one distance.

Cardinal and Ordinal Directions

Cardinal directions are the main four: north, south, east, and west. Ordinal directions are halfway between these points: northwest, northeast, southwest, southeast. Help students understand these directions further by using a compass to find north in your own classroom. While students usually quickly master the names and relationships of the directions to each other, they still struggle to apply those directions to one place on a map in relation to another. An interesting cultural note: Saying the directions in the order of North, South, East, and West is a "western" tradition. Many cultures use a different order. For example, the Navajo always start with East and continue clockwise to North. Ask your second-language learners how they learned the directions. Taking a moment to discuss them may help students connect the "old" directions to the "new" ones.

Mapping the United States and Canada

While the maps in this book are a great start for exploring the United States and Canada, students should be given an opportunity to explore further. Consider bringing in a variety of road atlases for students to look through. Include atlases that show entire states as well as Thomas's guides, which show a single county in incredible detail. Online map generators are also a fun way for students to explore their own community.

Name_____ Date_____

North America

Use the map to complete the activities.

Did you know? Hawaii is part of the United States but it is not considered part of North America.

1. On this map there are two special lines of latitude indicated by dashed lines. The first is the Tropic of Cancer. The second is the Arctic circle. Label those.

2. Label the North Pole 90°N.

3. The line of latitude just below the Tropic of Cancer is 20°N. Each line north of it is 20 additional degrees. Label them.

4. Label Canada, The United States, and Mexico. Shade Canada green, The United States dark blue, and Mexico red. Be sure to include Alaska with the United States.

5. Distinguish between land and water by coloring all of the water light blue. Include major inland bodies of water such as the Great Lakes. Use a globe for reference.

6. The meridian that passes through the center of Greenland (Northeast of Canada) is 40°W. The other meridians on this map are also 20° apart, increasing in value as you go west. Label each meridian.

7. Is the prime meridian on this map? Why or why not?

_____

8. Explain why the half of the map east of 100°W is not in the eastern hemisphere.

_____

9. What country is found where 80°N and 20°W intersect?

_____

10. What country is found where 20°N and 100°W intersect?

_____

Maps: United States and Canada © 2005 Creative Teaching Press

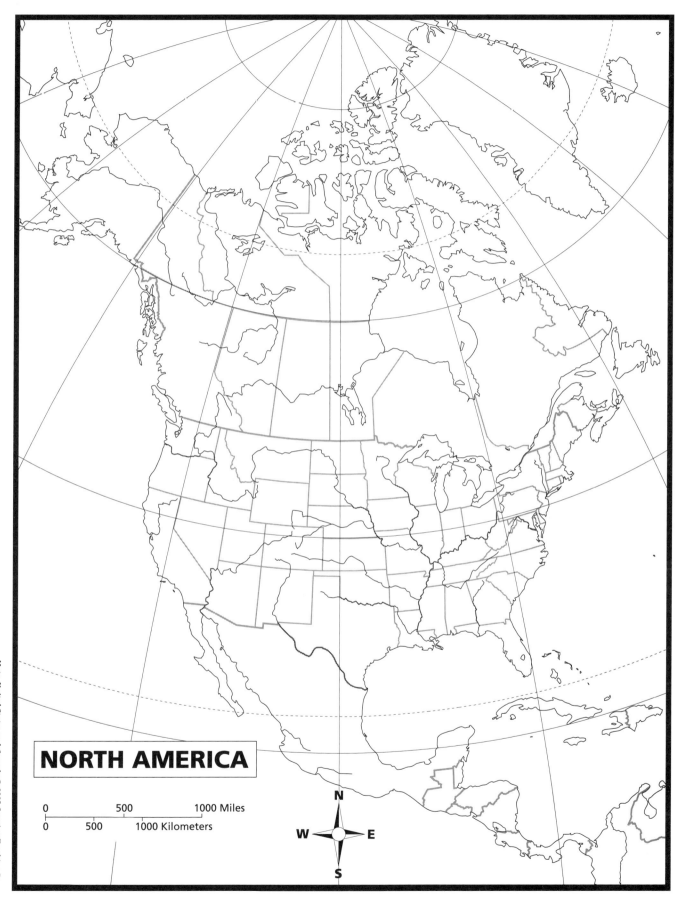

NORTH AMERICA

| 0 | | 500 | | 1000 Miles |
| 0 | 500 | | 1000 Kilometers | |

N
W   E
S

Name_____   Date_____

The United States

Use the map to answer the questions.

Did you know? The Louisiana purchase covered the land between the Mississippi River and the Rocky Mountains. It was a huge parcel of land, but for a long time, its European owners didn't consider it worth much. France gave it to Spain and Spain gave it back to France. When the United States approached France for rights to navigating the Mississippi river, the French offered President Thomas Jefferson the entire parcel. Once acquired, the land was swiftly settled.

1. Use the following postal abbreviations to label each state and the capital on the map.

Alabama	AL	Kentucky	KY	North Dakota	ND
Alaska	AK	Louisiana	LA	Ohio	OH
Arizona	AZ	Maine	ME	Oklahoma	OK
Arkansas	AR	Maryland	MD	Oregon	OR
California	CA	Massachusetts	MA	Pennsylvania	PA
Colorado	CO	Michigan	MI	Rhode Island	RI
Connecticut	CT	Minnesota	MN	South Carolina	SC
Delaware	DE	Mississippi	MS	South Dakota	SD
Washington D.C.	DC	Missouri	MO	Tennessee	TN
Florida	FL	Montana	MT	Texas	TX
Georgia	GA	Nebraska	NE	Utah	UT
Hawaii	HI	Nevada	NV	Vermont	VT
Idaho	ID	New Hampshire	NH	Virginia	VA
Illinois	IL	New Jersey	NJ	Washington	WA
Indiana	IN	New Mexico	NM	West Virginia	WV
Iowa	IA	New York	NY	Wisconsin	WI
Kansas	KS	North Carolina	NC	Wyoming	WY

2. Which two territories eventually divided in to a southern and northern state?

_____   _____

3. Which five states border the Pacific Ocean? _____ _____

_____ _____ _____

4. Which thirteen states border Canada?

_____

_____

5. Which four states border Mexico?

_____ _____ _____ _____

Maps: United States and Canada © 2005 Creative Teaching Press

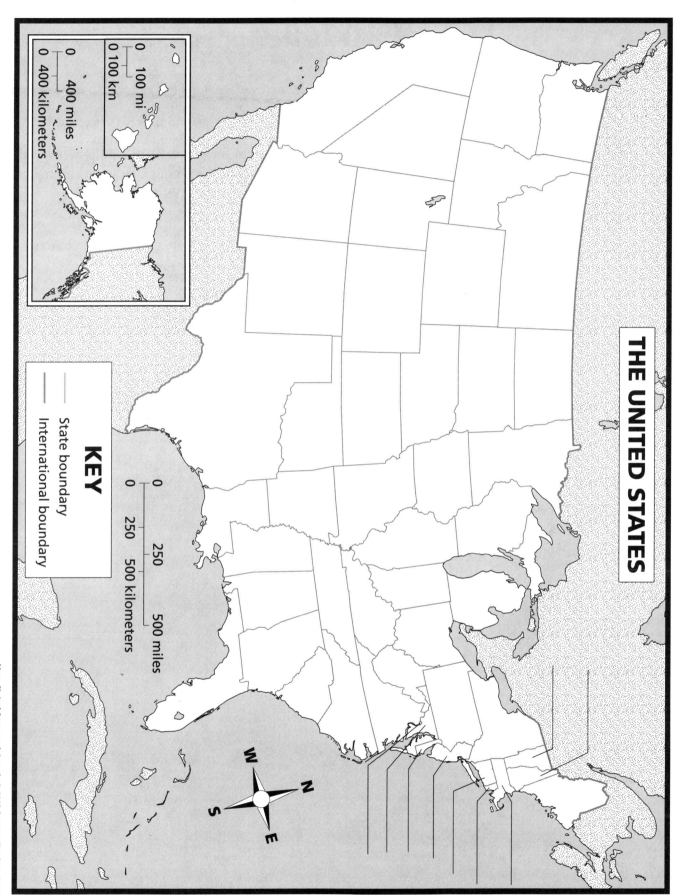

THE UNITED STATES

KEY

State boundary
International boundary

0   100 mi
0   100 km

0   400 miles
0   400 kilometers

0   250   500 miles
0   250   500 kilometers

Canada

Read the paragraph for background information. Then, use the map to answer the questions.

Did you know? Canada is the second largest country in the world. However, it is also one of the most sparsely populated. Most of the population lives in the southern areas close to the United States border. Huge stretches of land to the north are relatively empty of humans, making it a refuge for plants and animals.

Canada has two official languages: French and English. Even in parts of Canada that are not as highly populated with French-speaking Canadians as Quebec, all signs are written in both French and English.

1. Is it possible to drive from Winnipeg to Saskatoon? How do you know?

   _____

2. Why does Toronto have a star next to it?

   _____

3. What is the approximate location in latitude and longitude of Regina? _____

4. Which town is closer to Saint John: Quebec or Halifax?   _____

5. What is the approximate distance between Inuvik and Dawson?   _____

6. Why aren't there many major highways in the northern part of the country?

   _____

7. Which town is located at approximately 54°N, 130°W?   _____

8. Which town is directly north of Vancouver?   _____

9. Name the Canadian Territories.

   _____

Maps: United States and Canada © 2005 Creative Teaching Press

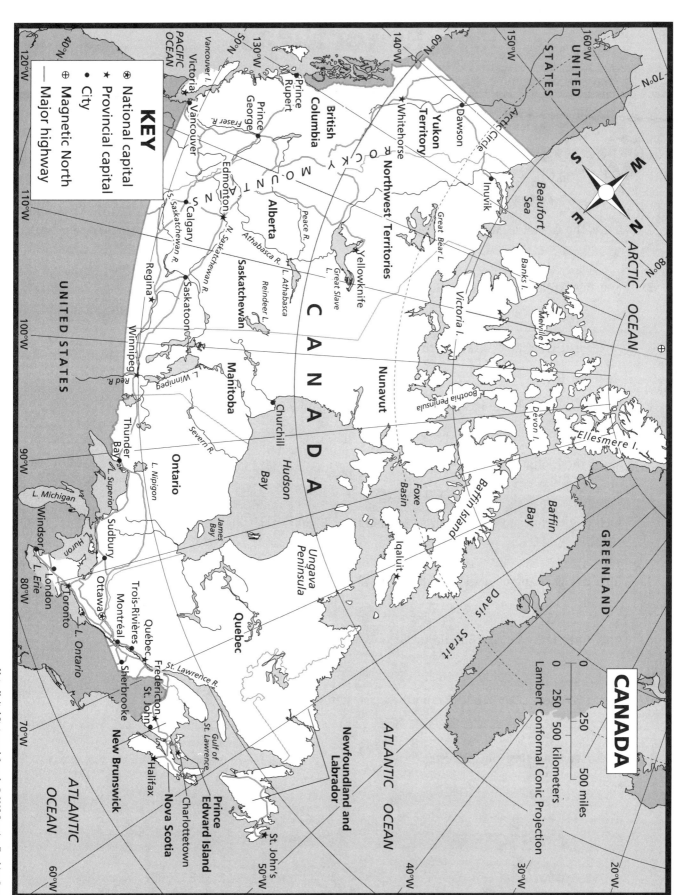

CANADA

Lambert Conformal Conic Projection

0   250   500 kilometers
0   250   500 miles

KEY
- ⊗ National capital
- ★ Provincial capital
- • City
- ⊕ Magnetic North
- — Major highway

Maps: United States and Canada © 2005 Creative Teaching Press

Name_____ Date_____

The Northeast

Use the map to answer the questions.

Did **you know?** Rhode Island is the smallest U.S. state, covering 1,212 sq mi (3,139 sq km). It may have been named after the Greek island of Rhodes or named Roode Eylandt (Red Island) by a Dutch explorer because of its red clay.

1. What is the capital of Massachusetts? _____

2. If you flew from Syracuse to Buffalo, which direction would you fly? _____

3. How far is it from New York City to Syracuse? _____

4. What is the approximate location in latitude and longitude of Watertown? _____

5. What is the capital of Rhode Island? _____

6. Which city is closer to Lake Ontario: Plattsburgh or Binghamton? _____

7. Which city is at approximately 42°N and 76°W? _____

8. Which Interstate connects Buffalo to Albany? _____

9. Which two Great Lakes are in the northeastern states?

   _____   _____

10. Which city is northeast of Augusta? _____

Maps: United States and Canada © 2005 Creative Teaching Press

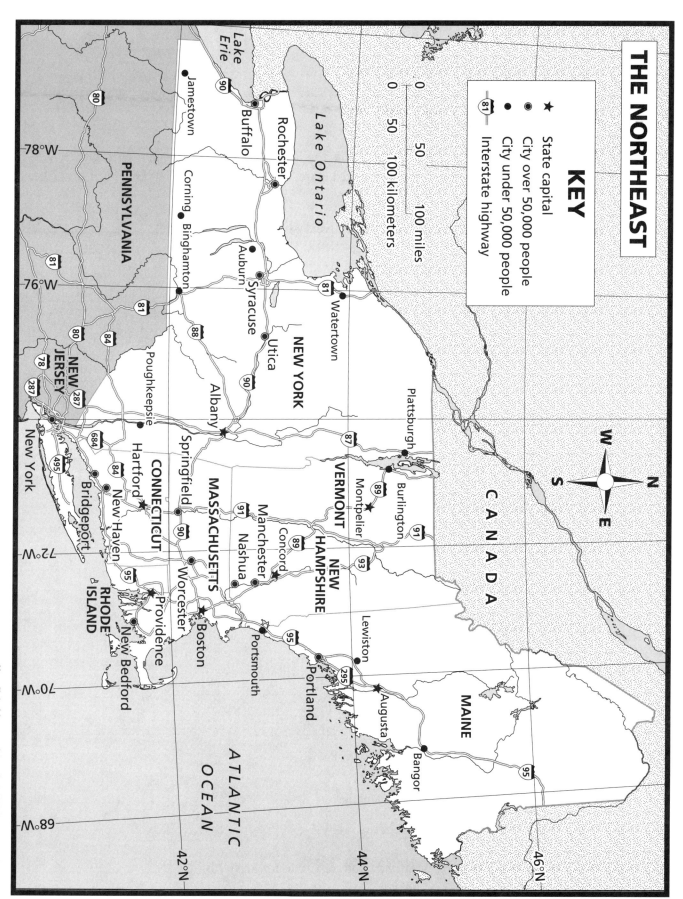

THE NORTHEAST

KEY

★ State capital
◉ City over 50,000 people
● City under 50,000 people
⟨81⟩ Interstate highway

0   50   100 kilometers
0   50   100 miles

CANADA

Lake Erie

Lake Ontario

PENNSYLVANIA

NEW JERSEY

NEW YORK

VERMONT

NEW HAMPSHIRE

MASSACHUSETTS

CONNECTICUT

RHODE ISLAND

MAINE

ATLANTIC OCEAN

Jamestown
Buffalo
Rochester
Corning
Binghamton
Auburn
Syracuse
Utica
Watertown
Albany
Poughkeepsie
New York
Bridgeport
New Haven
Hartford
Springfield
Worcester
Providence
New Bedford
Boston
Portsmouth
Portland
Lewiston
Augusta
Bangor
Plattsburgh
Burlington
Montpelier
Manchester
Concord
Nashua

78°W
76°W
72°W
70°W
68°W

42°N
44°N
46°N

90
80
81
88
84
78
287
684
495
84
95
90
87
89
91
93
89
95
295
95

N W S E

The South

Use the map to answer the questions.

Did you know? The Mississippi River is the largest river in North America. In 1783, it was the official western border of the United States. It flows 2,350 mi (3,780 km) until it reaches the Gulf of Mexico.

1. The capital city of Louisiana is on the Mississippi River. What is its name? _____

2. Which direction would you travel from Fayetteville to New Orleans? _____

3. If you lived in Columbus, which would be shorter: a trip to the beach on the Atlantic or on the Gulf of Mexico?
    _____

4. If you went swimming in Virginia Beach, what body of water would you be in? _____

5. Which city is located at approximately 26°N and 80.5°W? _____

6. Which 3 Interstate Highways would you take to drive from Atlanta to Louisville?
    _____   _____   _____

7. What is the capital city of Alabama? _____

8. Approximately how far is it from Lexington to Tallahassee? _____

9. Interstate 65 travels which direction from Mobile? _____

10. What is the approximate location in latitude and longitude for Memphis? _____

Maps: United States and Canada © 2005 Creative Teaching Press

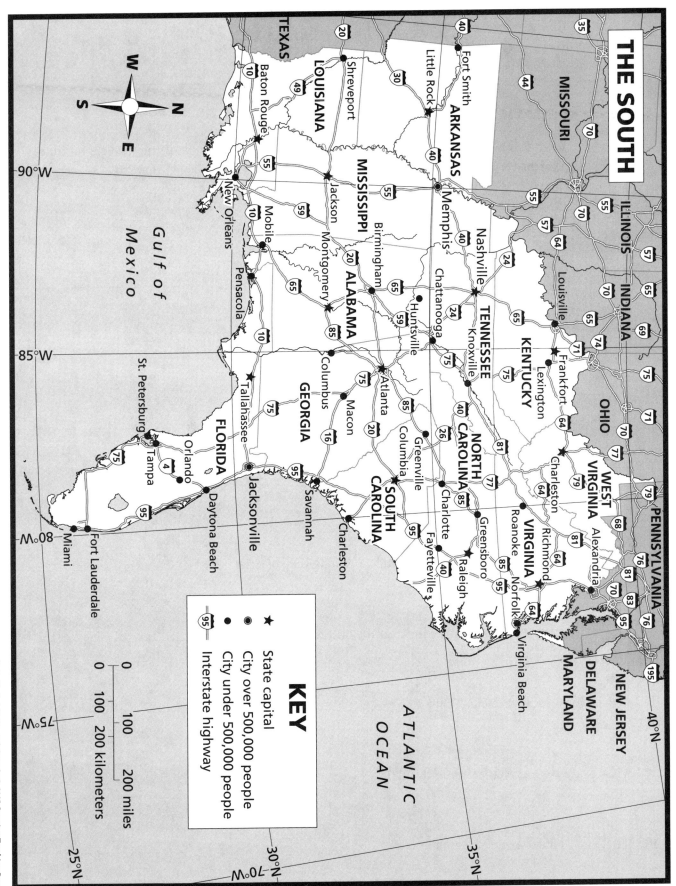

KEY

- ★ State capital
- ◉ City over 500,000 people
- ● City under 500,000 people
- 〰95〰 Interstate highway

Gulf of Mexico

ATLANTIC OCEAN

The Mid-Atlantic

Use the map to answer the questions.

Did you know? Philadelphia was an important city in the time of the struggle for independence from Britain. The Declaration of Independence was signed there. It was even the capital city of the United States from 1790–1800.

1. Does Allentown have fewer than 50,000 people?   _____

2. Approximately how far is it from Reading to Philadelphia?   _____

3. What is closer to Williamsport: State College or Scranton?   _____

4. Is the national capital east or west of Annapolis?   _____

5. New Jersey and Delaware border which ocean?   _____

6. What is the approximate location in latitude and longitude of Erie?   _____

7. Roughly how far is it from Philadelphia to the current national capital?   _____

8. Which city is located at 40.5°N and 80°W?   _____

9. What is the state capital of Pennsylvania?   _____

10. What city is northeast of Trenton?   _____

Maps: United States and Canada © 2005 Creative Teaching Press

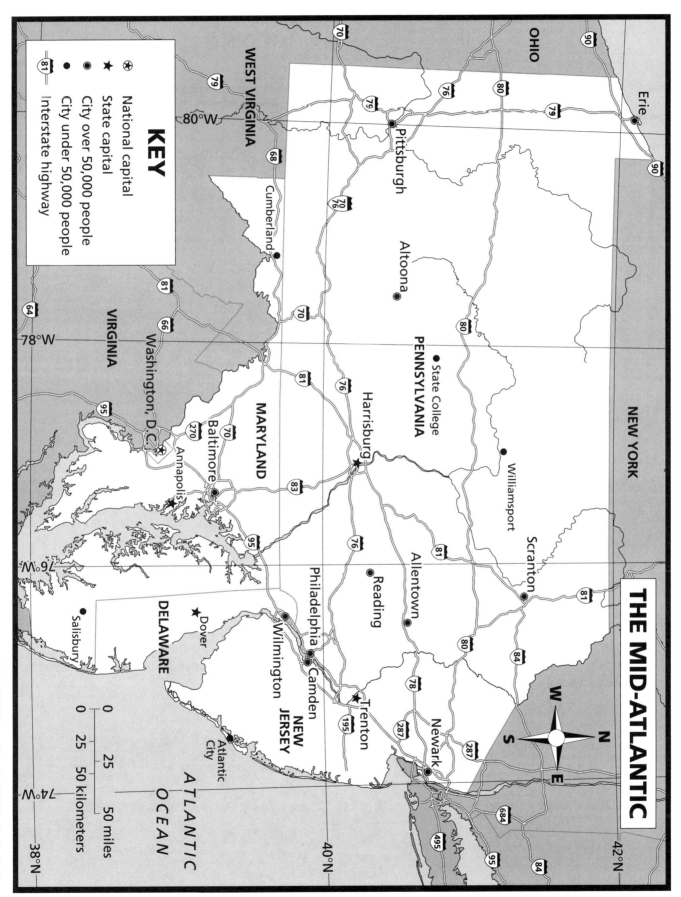

THE MID-ATLANTIC

KEY

⊗ National capital
★ State capital
◉ City over 50,000 people
● City under 50,000 people
Interstate highway

OHIO

WEST VIRGINIA

Erie

80°W

Pittsburgh

Cumberland

Altoona

PENNSYLVANIA

● State College

Williamsport

NEW YORK

Scranton

VIRGINIA

78°W

Washington, D.C.

Baltimore

Annapolis

MARYLAND

Harrisburg

Allentown

Reading

Philadelphia

76°W

Salisbury

DELAWARE

★ Dover

Wilmington

Camden

NEW JERSEY

Trenton

Newark

Atlantic City

ATLANTIC OCEAN

40°N

42°N

38°N

74°W

N
W   E
S

0   25   50 miles
0   25   50 kilometers

Maps United States and Canada © 2005 Creative Teaching Press

The Great Lakes

Use the map to answer the questions.

Did you know? Lake Superior is the largest source of freshwater in the world. If you emptied out the other four Great Lakes, Lake Superior would have enough water to refill them . . . as well as have a little left over for itself! The Great Lakes have always been an important route to transport people and goods, and they're almost as famous for their shipwrecks as they are for their beauty.

1. Is the population of the Canadian city of Sault Ste. Marie more than 50,000? _____

2. Approximately how far is the eastern shore of Lake Michigan from Milwaukee? _____

3. A wind blowing from Peoria to Madison is traveling in which direction? _____

4. What is the capital of Michigan? _____

5. Which city would you find at approximately 40°N and 89.5°W? _____

6. A ship carrying goods from Escanaba to Traverse City would travel in which direction? _____

7. Which state capitals does the I70 cross? _____

8. Imagine you're a ship captain in Racine. You don't have much fuel in your engine. Would you rather travel to Gary or Sheboygan?

   _____

9. Champaign is in which state? _____

10. What is the approximate latitude and longitude of the western tip of Lake Superior? _____

Maps: United States and Canada © 2005 Creative Teaching Press

THE GREAT LAKES

CANADA

KEY

★ State capital
◉ City over 50,000 people
● City under 50,000 people
🛣 75 Interstate highway

0   50   100 miles
0   50   100 kilometers

MINNESOTA

Lake Superior

48°N
46°N

Superior

Marquette

Sault Ste. Marie

Escanaba

WISCONSIN

Eau Claire   Wausau

Green Bay

Appleton

44°N

La Crosse

Fond du Lac

Sheboygan

Lake Michigan

Alpena

Traverse City

Lake Huron

MICHIGAN

Saginaw

Grand Rapids

Flint

Lansing   Port Huron

Madison

IOWA

Milwaukee

Racine

Rockford

Kalamazoo

Detroit

Ann Arbor

Lake Erie

42°N

Chicago

Joliet   Gary   South Bend   Toledo

Cleveland   Youngstown

Akron

INDIANA

Fort Wayne

Mansfield   Lima

Canton

Peoria

Bloomington

Champaign

Muncie

OHIO

Quincy

40°N

Springfield   Decatur   Indianapolis

Dayton   Columbus

ILLINOIS   Terre Haute

Bloomington   Cincinnati

WEST VIRGINIA

70

MISSOURI

38°N

Evansville

Carbondale

KENTUCKY

N
W   E
S

VIRGINIA

92°W   90°W   88°W   86°W   84°W   82°W

The Midwest

Read the paragraph for background information. Then, use the map to answer the questions.

Did **you know**? If you'd like to look at an alien landscape, the Badlands in South Dakota might be a great place for you to visit. Very few plants grow in this rocky, harsh area, and flash floods have carved weirdly beautiful canyons. The Badlands are even full of fossils of strange creatures like the three-toed horse and the saber-toothed tiger.

1. Canada is what direction from Wichita?   _____

2. A bird flying from North Dakota to Ottumwa is going in which direction? _____

3. Which city has a larger population: Watertown or Waterloo?   _____

4. What is the approximate latitude and longitude of Dodge City?   _____

5. Rolla is located in which state?   _____

6. What is the approximate distance between Hibbing and Dodge City?   _____

7. What is the capital city of Iowa?   _____

8. What city would you find at approximately 47°N and 97°W?   _____

9. If you wanted to see the fossil of a three-toed horse, would you travel to Rapid City or Emporia?

_____   _____

10. Which is further from St Louis: Joplin or Fort Dodge?   _____

Maps: United States and Canada © 2005 Creative Teaching Press

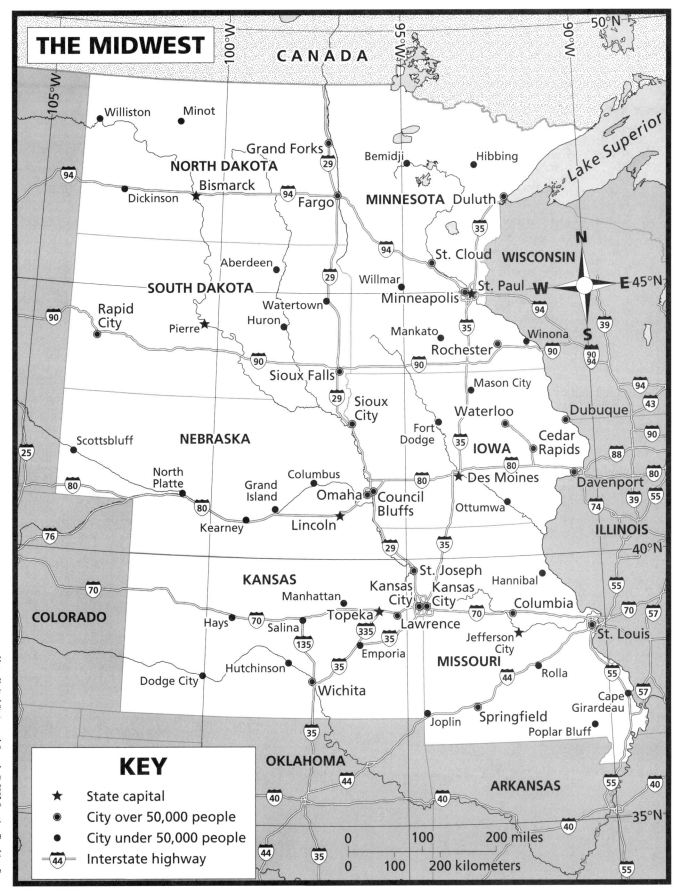

THE MIDWEST

CANADA

50°N

NORTH DAKOTA

Williston · Minot

Grand Forks

Bismarck
Dickinson

Fargo

94

MINNESOTA Duluth

Bemidji · Hibbing

Lake Superior

St. Cloud

WISCONSIN

SOUTH DAKOTA

Aberdeen

Willmar

Minneapolis St. Paul

45°N

Watertown
Huron

Rapid City

Pierre

Mankato

Rochester

Winona

Sioux Falls

Mason City

Dubuque

NEBRASKA

Sioux City

Waterloo

Cedar Rapids

Scottsbluff

Fort Dodge

IOWA

Davenport

North Platte

Columbus

Des Moines

Grand Island

Omaha

Council Bluffs

Ottumwa

Kearney

Lincoln

ILLINOIS

40°N

St. Joseph

Hannibal

KANSAS

Manhattan

Kansas City Kansas City

Columbia

COLORADO

Hays

Topeka

Lawrence

St. Louis

Salina

Jefferson City

Hutchinson

Emporia

MISSOURI

Rolla

Dodge City

Wichita

Cape Girardeau

OKLAHOMA

Joplin Springfield

Poplar Bluff

ARKANSAS

35°N

KEY

★ State capital

◉ City over 50,000 people

● City under 50,000 people

🛡 Interstate highway

0   100   200 miles

0   100   200 kilometers

Maps: United States and Canada © 2005 Creative Teaching Press

Name_____   Date_____

The Rocky Mountain States

Use the map to answer the questions.

Did **you know?** If you had a shovel and could travel back in time, these states might be the place to make you rich. 140 years ago gold, silver, and other valuable metals were discovered here. Many people moved into the Rocky Mountain area hoping to find their own buried treasure.

1. Which is further from the Pacific Ocean: Boise or Casper?   _____

2. Which direction would you travel from Pocatello to reach Fort Collins?   _____

3. What is the capital of Montana?   _____

4. Which state capital is directly south of Helena?   _____

5. If you wanted to sell the gold from your mine in Durango,
   what would be the nearest large city?   _____

6. What is the approximate latitude and longitude of Salt Lake City?   _____

7. How many cities are shown in Nevada?   _____

8. Approximately how far apart are Grand Junction and Montrose?   _____

9. Which city shown in Utah is closest to the boarder with Nevada?   _____

10. What city would you find at approximately 48.5°N and 110°W?   _____

Maps: United States and Canada © 2005 Creative Teaching Press

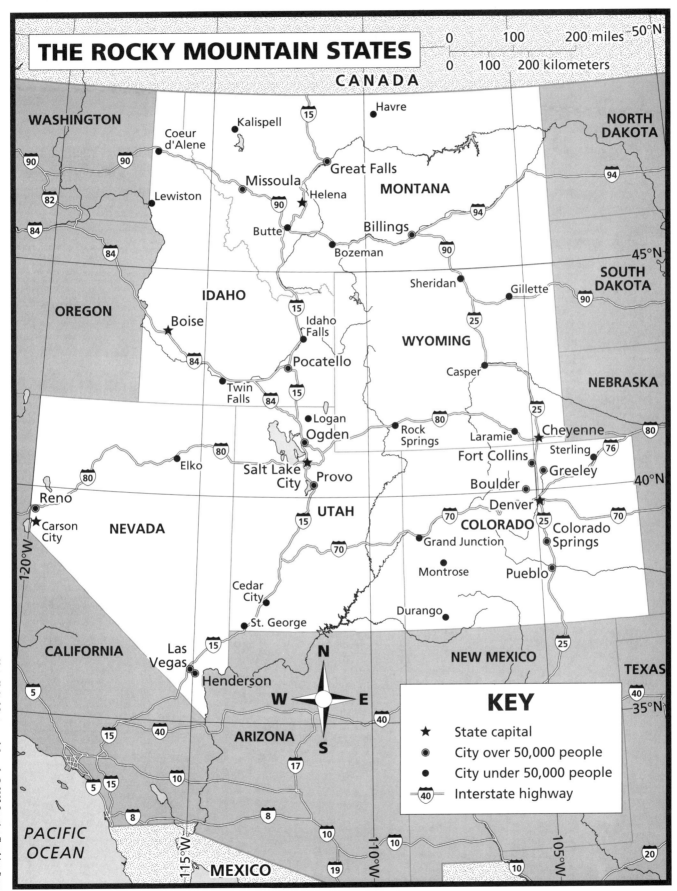

THE ROCKY MOUNTAIN STATES

0   100   200 miles
0   100   200 kilometers

CANADA

WASHINGTON

Kalispell
Havre

Coeur
d'Alene

Great Falls

Missoula
Helena
MONTANA

Lewiston

Butte
Billings

Bozeman

NORTH
DAKOTA

SOUTH
DAKOTA

Sheridan
Gillette

OREGON

IDAHO

Boise
Idaho
Falls

Pocatello

WYOMING

Casper

NEBRASKA

Twin
Falls

Logan
Ogden
Rock
Springs
Laramie
Cheyenne

Elko
Salt Lake
City
Provo
Fort Collins
Sterling
Greeley

Reno

Boulder

Carson
City

NEVADA
UTAH

Denver
COLORADO
Colorado
Springs

Grand Junction

Montrose
Pueblo

Cedar
City

Durango

St. George

CALIFORNIA

Las
Vegas
Henderson

NEW MEXICO

TEXAS

ARIZONA

KEY

★   State capital

◉   City over 50,000 people

●   City under 50,000 people

🛡 40   Interstate highway

PACIFIC
OCEAN

MEXICO

50°N

45°N

40°N

35°N

120°W   115°W   110°W   105°W

Maps United States and Canada © 2005 Creative Teaching Press

The West

Use the map to answer the questions.

Did **you know?** Without the Oregon Trail, Washington, Oregon and California might never have become part of the United States. This 2,000 mile (3,200 km) route was the only way to get from the mid-west to the west. Many settlers walked barefoot the entire way—through deserts and over mountains!

1. How many cities larger than 50,000 people does California have? _____

2. What city would you find at 45°N and 123°W? _____

3. What is the state capital of Washington? _____

4. Salinas is which direction from Bellingham? _____

5. Is Port Angeles or Colville closer to Klamath Falls? _____

6. The Dalles is a city on the Oregon Trail route.
   Approximately how far would you have to walk barefoot to reach the coast? _____

7. Oakland is directly east of which city? _____

8. How far is it between Redding and Spokane? _____

9. What is the approximate latitude and longitude of Barstow, California? _____

10. Which direction would you travel from the nearest coast to Ontario? _____

Maps: United States and Canada © 2005 Creative Teaching Press

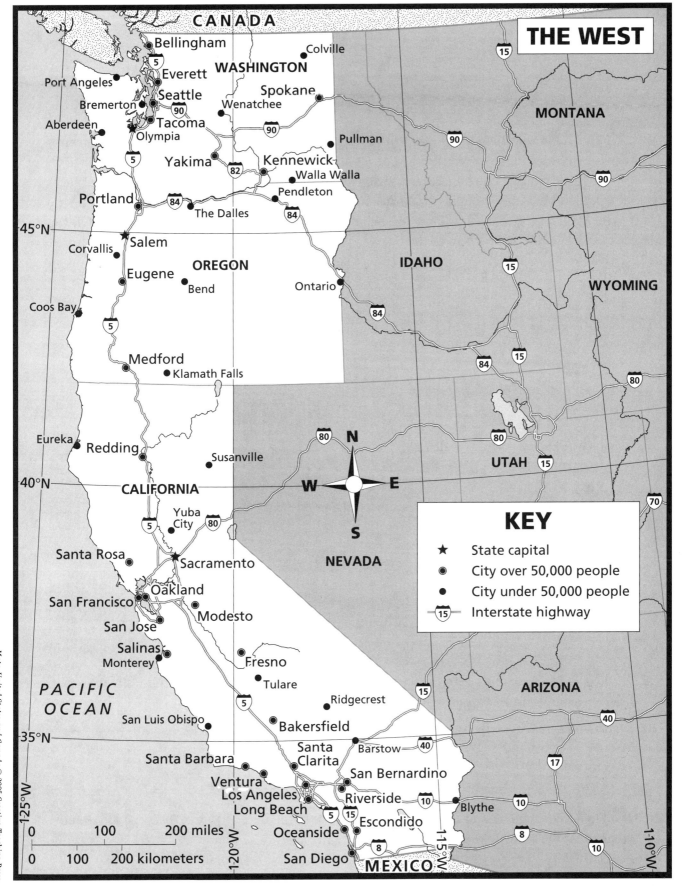

THE WEST

CANADA

Bellingham
Colville

WASHINGTON

Port Angeles
Everett
Spokane
Seattle
Wenatchee
Bremerton
Tacoma
Pullman
Aberdeen
Olympia
Yakima
Kennewick
Walla Walla
Pendleton
Portland
The Dalles

45°N
Corvallis
Salem
OREGON
Eugene
Bend
Coos Bay
Ontario

Medford
Klamath Falls

MONTANA

IDAHO

WYOMING

Eureka
Redding
Susanville
UTAH

40°N
CALIFORNIA
Yuba City

Santa Rosa
Sacramento
NEVADA
Oakland
San Francisco
Modesto
San Jose
Salinas
Monterey
Fresno
Tulare
PACIFIC OCEAN
Ridgecrest
ARIZONA
San Luis Obispo
Bakersfield
35°N
Santa Barbara
Santa Clarita
Barstow
Ventura
San Bernardino
Los Angeles
Riverside
Long Beach
Blythe
Escondido
Oceanside
San Diego
MEXICO

KEY

★ State capital
◉ City over 50,000 people
● City under 50,000 people
⌐15⌐ Interstate highway

0   100   200 miles
0   100   200 kilometers

125°W   120°W   115°W   110°W

Name_____ Date_____

The Southwest

N W E S

Use the map to answer the questions.

Did you know? In the mid 1800's President Polk declared war on Mexico after Mexico refused to sell California, the last bit of Texas, and the land in between to the United States. His primary general, Zachary Taylor, won nearly every battle in which he engaged the Mexican army, but he became well known for his unwillingness to pursue the Mexican army into their own country. (He felt it would be unethical.) At the end of the war, the U.S. had acquired the land and Taylor succeeded President Polk as president of the U.S.

1. What is the distance from Flagstaff, AZ to Gallup, NM?   _____

2. What would be the most direct route from Houston, TX to Tucson, AZ?   _____

3. Which states border Texas?   _____

4. Which cities shown on the map border Mexico?   _____

5. Which body of water provides Texas with the fourth-longest coastline for a U.S. state? _____

6. Which city is found at approximately 31.5°N and 109°W?   _____

7. What are the approximate coordinates of Houston, TX?   _____

8. What appears to be the only major highway out of Lubbock, TX? Is it likely that this is really the only major highway out of Lubbock? Explain.

    _____

9. List the state capitals of the southwest states.

    _____

10. The Rio Grande originates in the mountains and flows to the Gulf of Mexico. Does the Rio Grande originate in the southwest? In which state does it originate?

    _____

Maps: United States and Canada © 2005 Creative Teaching Press

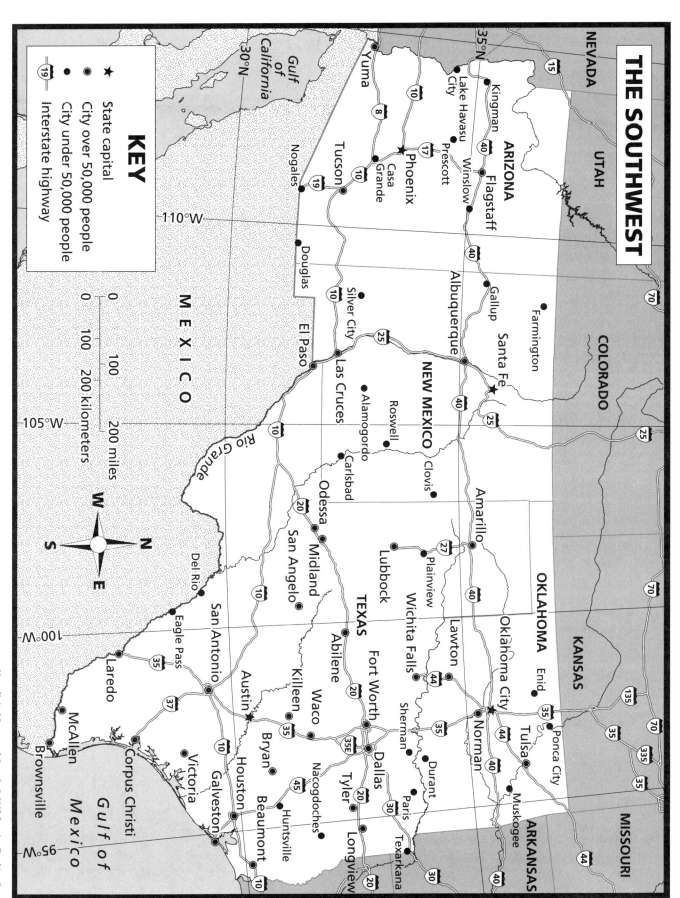

THE SOUTHWEST

KEY

★ State capital
◉ City over 50,000 people
● City under 50,000 people
⑲ Interstate highway

NEVADA

UTAH

ARIZONA

Yuma

Lake Havasu City

Kingman

Prescott

Winslow

Flagstaff

Phoenix

Casa Grande

Tucson

Nogales

Douglas

Gulf of California

M E X I C O

Gulf of Mexico

El Paso

Las Cruces

Silver City

Alamogordo

Roswell

Carlsbad

NEW MEXICO

Gallup

Albuquerque

Santa Fe

Farmington

COLORADO

Clovis

Amarillo

Plainview

Lubbock

Wichita Falls

Lawton

OKLAHOMA

Oklahoma City

Norman

Enid

KANSAS

Ponca City

Tulsa

Muskogee

Durant

ARKANSAS

MISSOURI

Sherman

Dallas

Paris

Texarkana

Longview

Tyler

Nacogdoches

Huntsville

Beaumont

Galveston

Houston

Bryan

Austin

Killeen

Waco

Abilene

Fort Worth

TEXAS

Midland

Odessa

San Angelo

San Antonio

Laredo

Eagle Pass

Del Rio

Rio Grande

Victoria

Corpus Christi

McAllen

Brownsville

Odessa

30°N

35°N

110°W

105°W

100°W

95°W

0   100   200 miles
0   100   200 kilometers

N S E W

Maps United States and Canada © 2005 Creative Teaching Press

The Southwest   29

Alaska

Use the map to answer the questions.

Did you know? Alaska is the only state far enough north to be in the "land of the midnight sun". In Barrow the sun does not set for 84 days in summer!

1. Approximately how far is it between Fairbanks to Mt. McKinley?   _____

2. Name a city over 30,000 people.   _____

3. What city is located at 58°N and 152°W?   _____

4. Which direction would you travel from Bethel to reach the Canadian boarder?   _____

5. Which is further from Fairbanks: the Gulf of Alaska or the Arctic Ocean?   _____

6. What do we call the body of water dividing Alaska and Russia?   _____

7. Alaska has large deposits of its state gem, jade. There is even an entire mountain of jade on the Seward Peninsula. What is the approximate latitude and longitude of the city of Seward?   _____

8. Which is the most northernmost city shown on the map?   _____

9. What is the capital city of Alaska?   _____

10. If you were to race your team of sled dogs from Fort Yukon to Barrow, what direction would you travel?   _____

Maps: United States and Canada © 2005 Creative Teaching Press

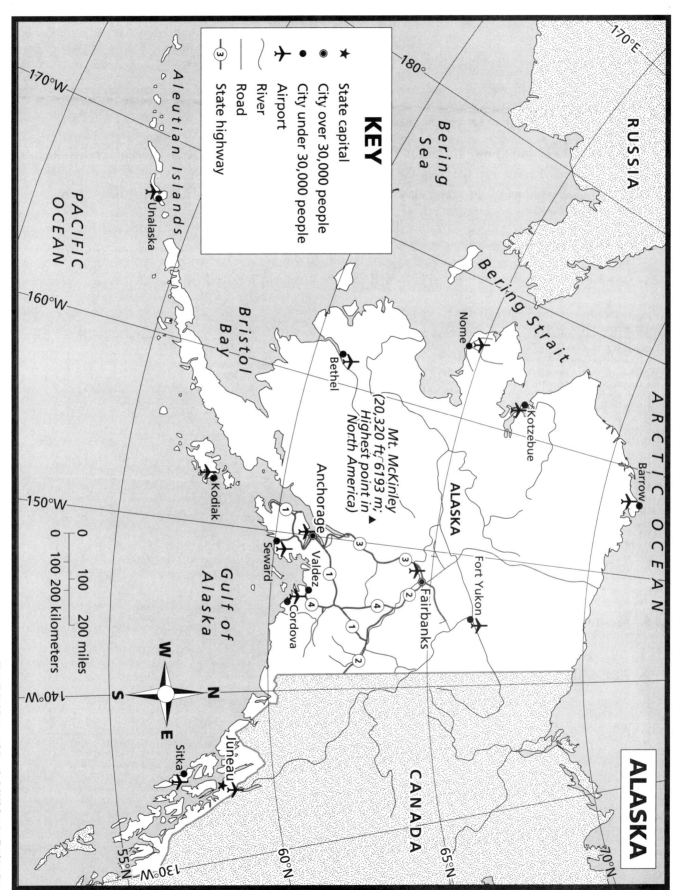

ALASKA

KEY

★ State capital
◉ City over 30,000 people
● City under 30,000 people
✈ Airport
〰 River
— Road
③ State highway

PACIFIC OCEAN

Aleutian Islands

Unalaska

Bering Sea

RUSSIA

Bering Strait

ARCTIC OCEAN

Bristol Bay

Nome

Kotzebue

Barrow

ALASKA

Bethel

Mt. McKinley
(20,320 ft; 6193 m;
Highest point in
North America) ▲

Anchorage

Fort Yukon

Kodiak

Seward

Valdez

Fairbanks

Cordova

Gulf of Alaska

CANADA

Sitka

Juneau

0   100   200 miles
0 100 200 kilometers

N
W   E
S

170°E
180°
170°W
160°W
150°W
140°W
130°W
170°E
55°N
60°N
65°N
70°N

Maps United States and Canada © 2005 Creative Teaching Press

Hawaii

Use the map to answer the questions.

Did you know? The island of Hawaii has the world's largest active volcanic crater—Kilauea. But don't worry; the frequent eruptions are usually contained in the boiling lake of lava at the bottom of the crater. Hawaiian stories say that Pele, the goddess of fire, lives there.

1. How many of Hawaii's cities have non-Hawaiian names? _____

2. In which direction from the island of Hawaii does the island chain extend? _____

3. Kahoolawe lies in which direction from Lanai? _____

4. What city would you find at 21°N and 157°W? _____

5. What is the distance between the shores of Niihau and Kahoolawe? _____

6. Is the capital city on the largest island? _____

7. If you wanted to travel from Makaha to visit the Kilauea crater on Hawaii, which direction would you travel? _____

8. Which is further from Kaunakakai: Holualoa or Lihue? _____

9. What is the approximate latitude and longitude of Kekaha? _____

10. What kind of road is highway 83? _____

Maps: United States and Canada © 2005 Creative Teaching Press

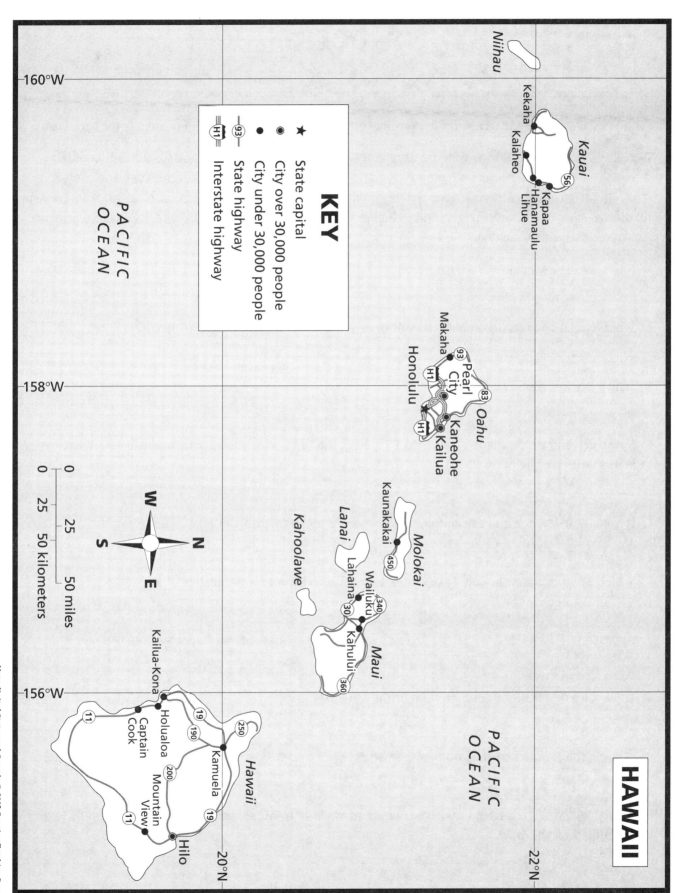

HAWAII

KEY

★ State capital
◉ City over 30,000 people
● City under 30,000 people
═ State highway
═ Interstate highway

PACIFIC
OCEAN

N
W   E
S

0   25   50 miles
0   25   50 kilometers

Niihau

Kauai
Kekaha
Kalaheo
Kapaa
Hanamaulu
Lihue
56

Oahu
Makaha
93
Honolulu
Pearl
City
H1
83
Kaneohe
Kailua
H1

Molokai
Kaunakakai
450
Lanai
Lahaina
Wailuku
340
Kahoolawe
Maui
Kahului
30
360

Hawaii
Kailua-Kona
11
Holualoa
Captain
Cook
19
190
250
Kamuela
200
Mountain
View
11
19
Hilo

PACIFIC
OCEAN

160°W
158°W
156°W

22°N
20°N

PACIFIC
OCEAN

Maps: United States and Canada © 2005 Creative Teaching Press

Alberta

Read the paragraph for background information. Then, use the map to answer the questions.

Did you know? Alberta, Canada is known around the world for its beautiful mountain scenes. It is a sort of gateway to Artic exploration and has rich oil, gas, coal, and timber resources. Alberta's river systems produced steeply eroded sedimentary rock. In these are found many dinosaur bones. Although it has a nice climate with more sunshine than any other Canadian province, Alberta remains sparsely populated.

1. What does the symbol ⚜ mean?

_____

2. What part of the reading would lead you to expect a park like Dinosaur Provincial Park?

_____

3. Which town is found at 3B on the map?   _____

4. If you drive north on highway 40 from Grande Cache (4A), which town will you come to? What happens to highway 40?

_____

5. If you are in the town of Edmonton, which possible highways can you take to leave town?

_____

6. Which town is closest to Cold Lake: Lac la Biche, Vegreville, or Lloydminster? _____

7. Approximately how far would you drive along Highway 93 to get from Jasper to Lake Louise?

_____

8. Is the town of Athabasca north or south of the Athabasca River?   _____

9. What is the location on the grid of Athabasca?   _____

10. How would you tell a friend to drive from Rainbow Lake to Athabasca, if they wanted to go by Fort Vermillion on the way?

_____

Maps: United States and Canada © 2005 Creative Teaching Press

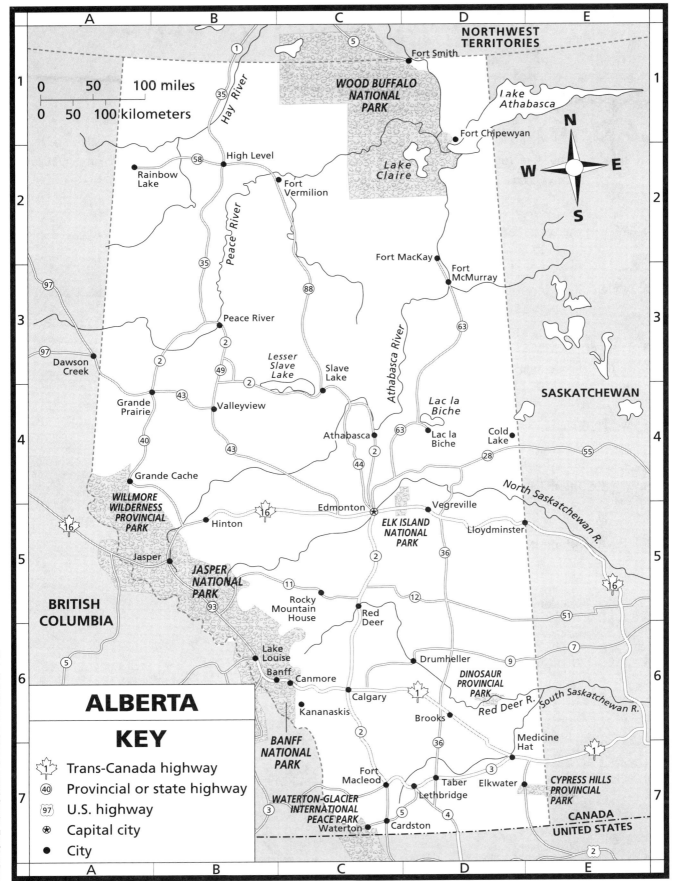

NORTHWEST TERRITORIES

1 Fort Smith

WOOD BUFFALO NATIONAL PARK

Lake Athabasca

Fort Chipewyan

Lake Claire

Hay River

Rainbow Lake

High Level

Fort Vermilion

Peace River

Fort MacKay

Fort McMurray

Peace River

Slave Lake

Lesser Slave Lake

Athabasca River

Lac la Biche

SASKATCHEWAN

Dawson Creek

Grande Prairie

Valleyview

Athabasca

Lac la Biche

Cold Lake

Grande Cache

North Saskatchewan R.

WILLMORE WILDERNESS PROVINCIAL PARK

Hinton

Edmonton

Vegreville

Lloydminster

ELK ISLAND NATIONAL PARK

Jasper

JASPER NATIONAL PARK

BRITISH COLUMBIA

Rocky Mountain House

Red Deer

Lake Louise

Banff

Canmore

Calgary

Drumheller

DINOSAUR PROVINCIAL PARK

Red Deer R.

South Saskatchewan R.

Kananaskis

Brooks

Medicine Hat

BANFF NATIONAL PARK

Fort Macleod

Taber

Lethbridge

Elkwater

CYPRESS HILLS PROVINCIAL PARK

WATERTON-GLACIER INTERNATIONAL PEACE PARK

Waterton

Cardston

CANADA
UNITED STATES

ALBERTA
KEY

🍁 1 Trans-Canada highway
40 Provincial or state highway
97 U.S. highway
⊛ Capital city
● City

0   50   100 miles
0   50   100 kilometers

N
W   E
S

Canada's Atlantic Coast

Use the map to answer the questions.

Did you know? Newfoundland is in a class all by itself. It's the only place in Canada to be in a split time zone. It is half an hour later than the rest of the Atlantic Time Zone. So if it is 2:00 pm in Nova Scotia, it is 2:30 pm in Newfoundland. Most other times zones are in one hour divisions.

1. What is the capital of the province of Nova Scotia? _____

2. Which city is located at approximately 46°N and 67°E? _____

3. From Prince Edward Island, would it be further to sail
   to the Isles de la Madeleine or St. Pierre & Miquelon? _____

4. Which direction is Cape Breton Island from Sable Island? _____

5. What is the name of the river that connects the city of Quebec to the ocean? _____

6. How far would it be to swim from Digby to Saint John? _____

7. Which direction would you sail to get from Cambellton to Battle Harbour? _____

8. If it is 4:30 in Grand Bank, what time is it in Edmundston? _____

9. What are the approximate latitude and longitude coordinates for Moncton? _____

10. What is the capital of the province of Newfoundland and Labrador? _____

Maps United States and Canada © 2005 Creative Teaching Press

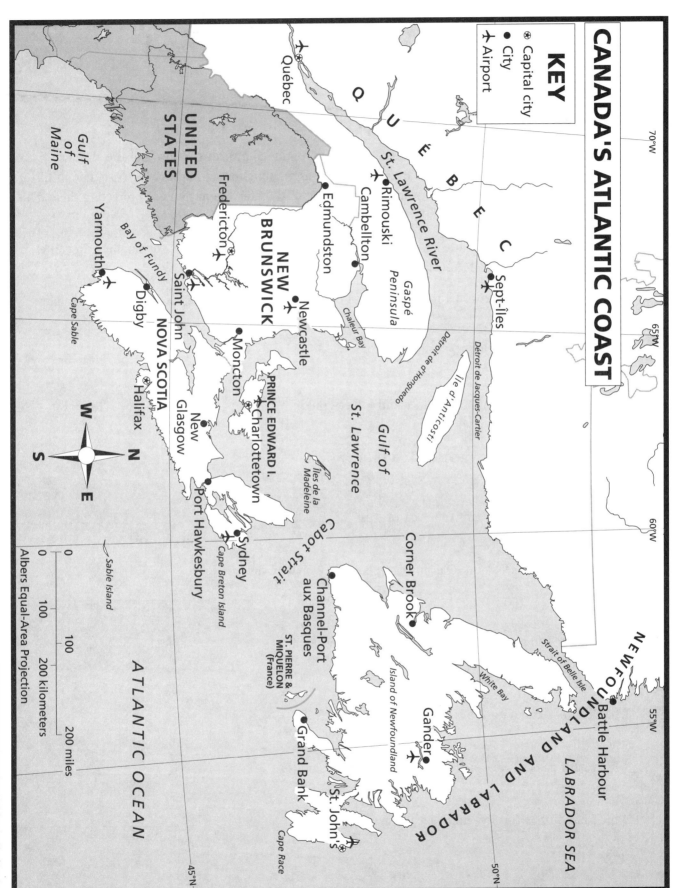

CANADA'S ATLANTIC COAST

KEY
⊗ Capital city
• City
✈ Airport

QUÉBEC

Québec ✈

St. Lawrence River

UNITED STATES

Gulf of Maine

Rimouski
Cambellton ✈
Edmundston •

Gaspé Peninsula

Chaleur Bay

Détroit de Jacques-Cartier

Sept-Îles ✈

Île d'Anticosti

Gulf of St. Lawrence

Fredericton ⊗✈

NEW BRUNSWICK

Newcastle ✈ •

Saint John ✈
Digby •
Yarmouth •
Cape Sable

Bay of Fundy

NOVA SCOTIA

Moncton •

New Glasgow •

Halifax ⊗

PRINCE EDWARD I.
Charlottetown ✈

Port Hawkesbury ✈

Cape Breton Island

Sydney ✈

Cabot Strait

Îles de la Madeleine

ST. PIERRE & MIQUELON (France)

Channel-Port aux Basques •

Corner Brook •

Strait of Belle Isle

White Bay

Island of Newfoundland

NEWFOUNDLAND AND LABRADOR

Battle Harbour •

LABRADOR SEA

Gander ✈ •

Grand Bank •

St. John's ⊗✈

Cape Race

ATLANTIC OCEAN

Sable Island

N W E S

70°W   65°W   60°W   55°W   50°N   45°N

0   100   200 kilometers
0   100   200 miles

Albers Equal-Area Projection

Maps: United States and Canada © 2005 Creative Teaching Press

Yosemite National Park

Use the map to answer the questions.

Did you know? President Abraham Lincoln granted Yosemite Valley and the Mariposa Grove of Giant Sequoias to the State of California as a public trust. This was the first time in history that a federal government had set aside scenic lands for the purpose of protecting them. This led to the designation of Yellowstone as the first official national park a few years later.

Later, John Muir's struggle to halt the significant damage to the subalpine meadows surrounding Yosemite Valley resulted in the creation of Yosemite National Park on October 1, 1890.

1. What is the difference between a path represented by a dashed line and one represented by a dotted line?

   _____

2. What would you find at Glacier Point? _____

3. What kinds of sites are at Lower Pines and Upper Pines? _____

4. What buildings are located near the Post Office? _____

5. Which river crosses the map from east to west? _____

6. Can you travel Glacier Point Road in December? Why or why not?

   _____

7. If you wanted to go horseback riding, which campground would be the most convenient for you? _____

8. What kind of natural feature is represented by ≈? _____

9. Which path passes between Moran Point and Union Point? _____

10. Which building is furthest north on the map? _____

Maps United States and Canada © 2005 Creative Teaching Press

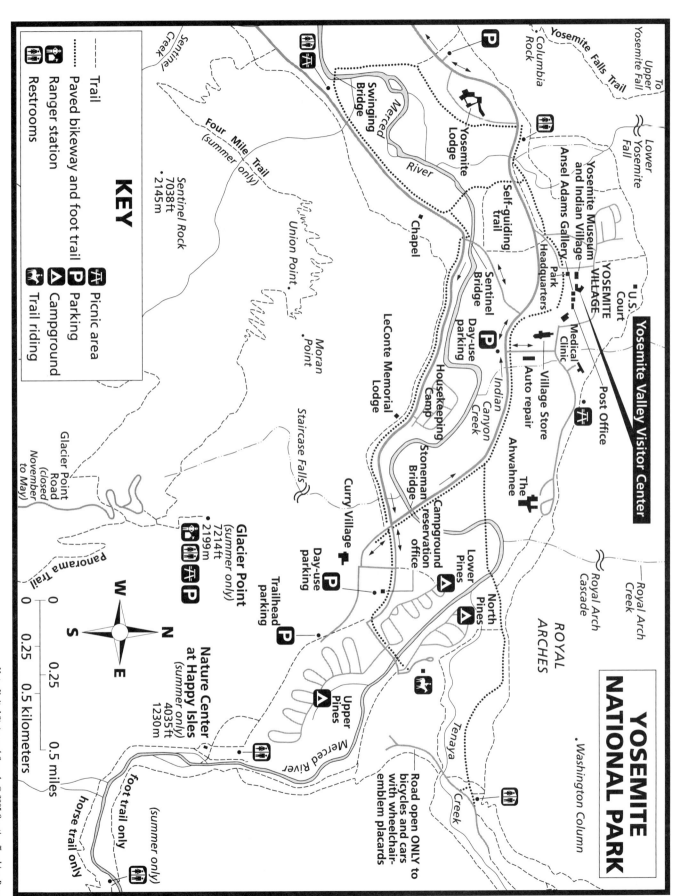

YOSEMITE NATIONAL PARK

Yosemite Valley Visitor Center

KEY

— — —	Trail	
··········	Paved bikeway and foot trail	
🅿	Parking	
🅰	Campground	
🏕	Ranger station	
🚻	Restrooms	
🅰	Picnic area	
🏇	Trail riding	

Sentinel Rock
7038ft
2145m

Four Mile Trail
(summer only)

Union Point

Moran Point

Staircase Falls

Glacier Point
(summer only)
7214ft
2199m

Glacier Point Road
(closed November to May)

Panorama Trail

Nature Center at Happy Isles
(summer only)
4035ft
1230m

foot trail only

horse trail only

(summer only)

Merced River

Trailhead parking

Day-use parking

Curry Village

LeConte Memorial Lodge

Upper Pines

Lower Pines

North Pines

Stoneman Bridge

Campground reservation office

Housekeeping Camp

Sentinel Bridge

Chapel

Sentinel Creek

Swinging Bridge

Merced River

Yosemite Lodge

Columbia Rock

To Upper Yosemite Fall

Yosemite Falls Trail

Lower Yosemite Fall

Self-guiding trail

Yosemite Museum and Indian Village

Ansel Adams Gallery

YOSEMITE VILLAGE

U.S. Court

Park Headquarters

Medical Clinic

Village Store

Auto repair

Post Office

The Ahwahnee

Indian Canyon Creek

Day-use parking

Royal Arch Cascade

Royal Arch Creek

ROYAL ARCHES

Washington Column

Tenaya Creek

Road open ONLY to bicycles and cars with wheelchair-emblem placards

N W E S

Scale:
0   0.25   0.5 kilometers
0   0.25   0.5 miles

Name_____   Date_____

Chicago, Illinois

Use the map to answer the questions.

Did you know? Jean-Baptiste Pointe du Sable, a fur trader from Haiti of African decent, founded a settlement called Eschikagou on the north bank of the Chicago River in 1772. He married a Potawatomi Indian woman and their daughter was Chicago's first birth in 1796.

1. To get from Itasca (C1) to Chicago O'Hare Airport, which road would you take? What highway is this as well?

   a. Irving Park Rd; State Highway 19
   b. Lake St; Hwy 20
   c. Busse Rd.; Hwy83
   d. Eisenhower Expwy; Hwy 290

2. If you landed at Midway Airport, which direction would you take to get to the Museum of Science and Industry?

   a. north
   b. south
   c. northwest
   d. east

3. What is the approximate distance from the Brookfield Zoo to Midway Airport?

   a. 4 mi or 4 km
   b. 6 mi or 9.5 km
   c. 9 km or 6.5 mi
   d. 2 mi or 4 km

4. What tourist attraction is located in C6?

   a. Wrigley Field
   b. U.S. Cellular Field
   c. Lincoln Park Zoo
   d. Art Institute

5. A relative of yours is coming to visit. You live in Oak Brook. This person can find Oak Brook looking at

   a. F4
   b. D4
   c. E2
   d. E4

6. The Sanitary and Ship Canal (G1) eventually connects with which river? In which quadrant of the map does it do so?

   a. Des Plaines River; E4
   b. Calumet River; G7
   c. Salt Creek; E4
   d. North Branch Chicago River; E6

Maps: United States and Canada © 2005 Creative Teaching Press

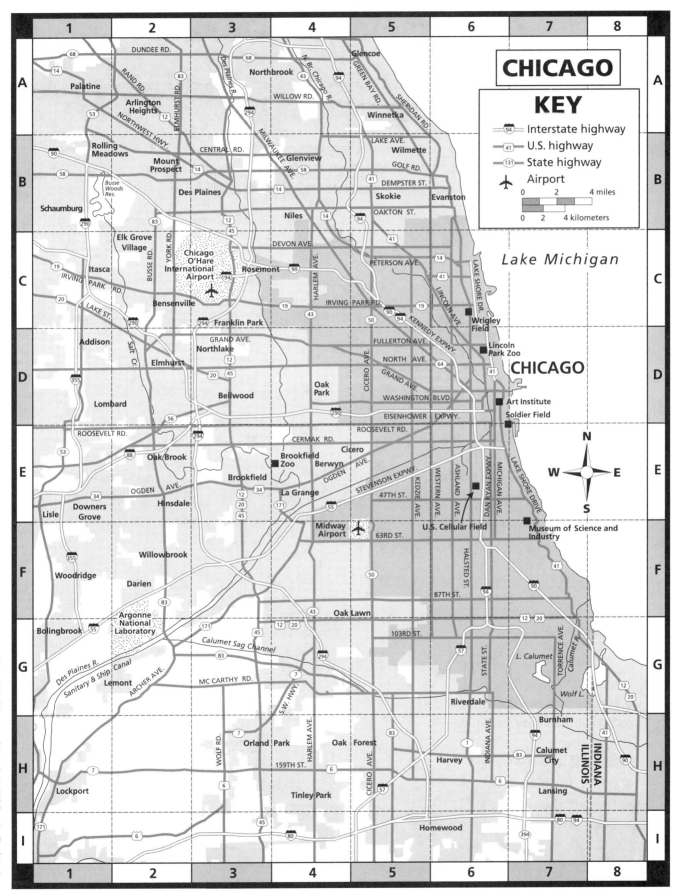

Los Angeles, California

Use the map to answer the questions.

Did you know? Los Angeles is the only city in the world divided in two by a mountain range, the Santa Monica Mountains. It also the only city divided by a national park. The Santa Monica Mountains National Recreation Area is the largest urban park, at 153,075 acres.

1. What section of the grid is Dodger Stadium in?

    a. A3
    b. D4
    c. B3
    d. E4

2. What university is in grid D4?

    a. Huntington College
    b. California State University—Northridge
    c. University of Southern California
    d. California State University—Long Beach

3. You have arrived at the Los Angeles International Airport. Which direction do you have to drive to get to the Mount Wilson Observatory?

    a. north
    b. northeast
    c. south
    d. southwest

4. How far is it from Griffith Park to the Huntington Library?

    a. 11 miles, 18 km
    b. 18 mi, 11 km
    c. 8 mi, 8 km
    d. 4 mi, 8 km

5. You are at the Los Angeles Maritime Museum. Is it farther to the Disney Studios or the 20th Century Fox Studios?

    a. 20th Century Fox Studios
    b. Disney Studios
    c. They are the same distance.
    d. These places are not in Los Angeles.

6. Give grid coordinates for the Santa Monica Mountains National Recreation Area.

    a. B1
    b. A1
    c. B4
    d. A4

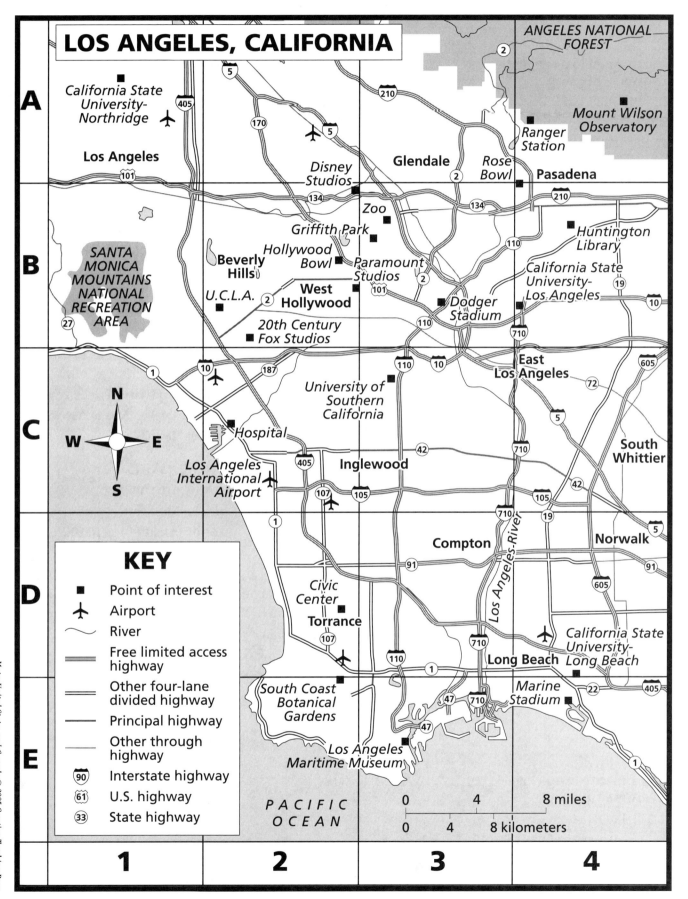

LOS ANGELES, CALIFORNIA

California State University-Northridge

Los Angeles

ANGELES NATIONAL FOREST

Mount Wilson Observatory

Ranger Station

Glendale

Rose Bowl

Pasadena

Disney Studios

Zoo

Griffith Park

Huntington Library

Hollywood Bowl

Beverly Hills

Paramount Studios

California State University-Los Angeles

SANTA MONICA MOUNTAINS NATIONAL RECREATION AREA

U.C.L.A.

West Hollywood

Dodger Stadium

20th Century Fox Studios

East Los Angeles

University of Southern California

Hospital

South Whittier

Los Angeles International Airport

Inglewood

Compton

Norwalk

Los Angeles River

Civic Center

Torrance

California State University-Long Beach

South Coast Botanical Gardens

Long Beach

Marine Stadium

Los Angeles Maritime Museum

PACIFIC OCEAN

KEY

- ■ Point of interest
- ✈ Airport
- ∿ River
- ═══ Free limited access highway
- ══ Other four-lane divided highway
- ── Principal highway
- — Other through highway
- 90 Interstate highway
- 61 U.S. highway
- 33 State highway

0   4   8 miles

0   4   8 kilometers

A   B   C   D   E

1   2   3   4

Answer Key

North America (Page 9)
Evaluate the Map
1. North America
2. the extent of North America and its major political boundaries.
3. political boundaries, land and water features, scale, compass rose, lat. and long.
4. 10°N, 90°N; 20°W, 160°W
5. 13/16":500 mi; 13 mm:500 km
6. answers will vary
7. answers will vary
8. Pacific Ocean
9. answers will vary

Activity Page
1. Check student work.
2. Check student work.
3. Students should label the lines 20°N, 40°N, 60°N, and 80°N.
4. Check student work.
5. Check student work.
6. students should label the lines 20°W, 40°W, 60°W, 80°W, 100°W, 120°W, 140°W, 160°W, 180°W
7. No, the Prime Meridian is 0°, which is not visible on this map.
8. The hemispheres are not determined by the placement of the compass rose on the map, but by their placement on the globe. This map only shows the northern and western hemispheres.
9. Greenland
10. Mexico

The United States (Page 11)
Evaluate the Map
1. The United States
2. the extent of the United States and its major physical features
3. political boundaries, land and water features, key, scale, compass rose
4. N/A
5. 3/4":250 mi; 12 mm:250 km
6. answers will vary
7. answers will vary
8. Atlantic Ocean
9. answers will vary

Activity Page
1. Have students compare their work to a map of the United States in an atlas.
2. the Dakotas and the Carolinas
3. Washington, Oregon, and California, Alaska, and Hawaii
4. Washington, Idaho, Montana, North Dakota, Minnesota, Wisconsin, Michigan, Ohio, Pennsylvania, New York, New Hampshire, Vermont, and Maine.
5. California, Arizona, New Mexico, and Texas

Canada (Page 13)
Evaluate the Map
1. Canada
2. the extent of Canada and its major physical features.
3. political boundaries, land and water features, key, scale, compass rose, grid lines, lat. and long., individual towns or cities
4. 40°N, 90°N; 20°W, 160°W
5. 5/8":250 mi; 9 mm:250 km
6. answers will vary
7. answers will vary
8. Atlantic Ocean
9. answers will vary

Activity Page
1. Yes, according to the key and map, there is a highway connecting them.
2. Toronto is the provincial capital of Ontario.
3. 50°N, 104°W
4. Halifax
5. ~350 mi, ~510 km
6. the northern section of Canada is very sparsely populated and does not support a major highway
7. Prince Rupert
8. Prince George
9. Alberta, British Columbia, Manitoba, New Brunswick, Newfoundland and Labrador, Northwest Territories, Nova Scotia, Nunavut, Ontario, Prince Edward Island, Quebec, Saskatchewan, Yukon Territory

The Northeast (Page 15)
Evaluate the Map
1. The Northeast
2. the extent of the Northeast region and its major physical features.
3. political boundaries, land and water features, key, scale, compass rose, lat. and long., individual towns or cities
4. 41°N, 47°N; 67°W, 80°W
5. 11/16":50 mi; 10 mm:50 km
6. answers will vary
7. answers will vary
8. Atlantic Ocean
9. answers will vary

Activity page
1. Boston
2. West
3. ~200 mi, ~320 km

4. 44°N, 76°W
5. Providence
6. Binghamton
7. Binghamton
8. I90
9. Lake Erie and Lake Ontario
10. Bangor

The South (Page 17)
Evaluate the Map
1. The South
2. the extent of the region of the South and its major physical and political features
3. political boundaries, land and water features, key, scale, compass rose, lat. and long., individual towns or cities
4. 25°N, 40°N; 70°W, 95°W
5. 5/8":100 mi; 9 mm:100 km
6. answers will vary
7. answers will vary
8. Atlantic Ocean
9. answers will vary

Activity Page
1. Baton Rouge
2. southwest
3. the Gulf of Mexico
4. the Atlantic Ocean
5. Miami, may also accept Ft. Lauderdale
6. I24, I65, and I75
7. Montgomery
8. ~530 mi, ~850km
9. northeast
10. 35°N, 90°W

The Mid-Atlantic (Page 19)
Evaluate the Map
1. The Mid-Atlantic
2. the extent of the Mid-Atlantic region and its physical and political features
3. political boundaries, land and water features, key, scale, compass rose, lat. and long., individual towns and cities
4. 38°N, 42°N; 74°W, 80°W
5. 9/16":25 mi; 9 mm:25 km
6. answers will vary
7. answers will vary
8. Atlantic Ocean
9. answers will vary
10. answers will vary

Activity Page
1. No
2. ~50 mi, ~80 km
3. State College
4. west
5. Atlantic Ocean
6. 42°N, 80°W
7. ~105 mi, ~185 km
8. Pittsburgh, PA
9. Harrisburg, PA
10. Newark, NJ

The Great Lakes (Page 21)
Evaluate the Map
1. The Great Lakes
2. the extent of the Great Lakes region and its major physical features
3. political boundaries, land and water features, key, scale, compass rose, lat. and long., individual towns or cities
4. 37°N, 49°N; 80°W, 92°W
5. 1/2":50 mi; 8 mm:50 km
6. answers will vary
7. answers will vary
8. Lake Superior
9. answers will vary

Activity Page
1. No
2. ~85 mi, ~137 km
3. north
4. Lansing
5. Springfield
6. southeast

7. Columbus and Indianapolis
8. Sheboygan
9. Illinois
10. 46.5°N, 92°W

The Midwest (Page 23)
Evaluate the Map
1. The Midwest
2. the extent of the Midwest region and its physical and political features
3. political boundaries, land and water features, key, scale, compass rose, lat. and long., individual towns or cities
4. 35°N, 50°N; 90°W, 105°W
5. 13/16":100 mi; 13 mm:100 km
6. answers will vary
7. answers will vary
8. Lake Superior
9. answers will vary

Activity Page
1. north
2. southeast
3. Waterloo
4. 38°N, 100°W
5. Missouri
6. ~765 mi, 1,230 km
7. Des Moines
8. Fargo
9. Rapid City, the badlands are in South Dakota
10. Fort Dodge

The Rocky Mountain States (Page 25)
Evaluate the Map
1. The Rocky Mountain States
2. the extent of the Rocky Mountain region and its major physical features
3. political boundaries, land and water features, key, scale, compass rose, lat. and long., individual towns and cities

4. 32°N, 50°N; 102°W, 120°W

5. 11/16":100 mi; 11 mm:100 km

6. answers will vary

7. answers will vary

8. Atlantic Ocean

9. answers will vary

Activity Page

1. Boise

2. southeast

3. Helena

4. Salt Lake City

5. Pueblo

6. 41°N, 112°W

7. 5

8. ~55 mi, ~88 km

9. St. George

10. Havre

The West (Page 27)
Evaluate the Map

1. The West

2. the extent of the region and its major physical features

3. political boundaries, political boundaries, land and water features, key, scale, compass rose, lat. and long., individual towns and cities

4. 34°N, 49°N; 110°W, 125°W

5. 3/4":100 mi; 12 mm:100 km

6. answers will vary

7. answers will vary

8. Pacific Ocean

9. answers will vary

Activity Page

1. 19; it is not possible to tell from the key if the state capitol is larger than 50,000

2. Salem, OR

3. Olympia

4. south

5. Port Angeles

6. 130 mi, 215 km

7. San Francisco

8. ~550 mi, ~885 km

9. 35°N, 117°W

10. East

The Southwest (Page 29)
Evaluate the Map

1. The Southwest

2. the extent of the Southwest region and its major physical features

3. political boundaries, land and water features, key, scale, compass rose, lat. and long., individual towns and cities

4. 25°N, 38°N; 94°W, 115°W

5. 11/16":100 mi; 10 mm:100 km

6. answers will vary

7. answers will vary

8. Gulf of Mexico

9. answers will vary

Activity page

1. ~164 mi, ~272 km

2. Hwy 10 traveling west

3. New Mexico, Oklahoma, Arkansas, Louisiana (unlabeled)

4. Nogales, AZ; Douglas, NM; El Paso, TX; Del Rio, TX; Eagle Pass, TX; Laredo, TX; McAllen, TX; Brownsville, TX

5. Gulf of Mexico

6. Douglas

7. 30°N, 95°W

8. Hwy 27; Possible answer: No, Lubbock is a city of over 50,000 people. If this map were a close-up of Lubbock, we would probably see the other highways that go in and out of the city.

9. Austin, TX; Oklahoma City, OK; Santa Fe, NM; Phoenix, AZ

10. No. It originates in Colorado.

Alaska (Page 31)
Evaluate the Map

1. Alaska

2. the extent of Alaska and its major physical features

3. political boundaries, land and water features, key, scale, compass rose, lat. and long., individual towns or cities, information specific to the people

4. 50°N, 70°N; 130°W, 170°W

5. 1/2":100 mi; 8 mm:100 km

6. answers will vary

7. answers will vary

8. Bering Sea

9. answers will vary

Activity Page

1. ~175 mi, ~300 km

2. Anchorage or Fairbanks, the map does not indicate whether Juneau is over or under 30,000. It is actually almost exactly 30,000.

3. Kodiak

4. east

5. Arctic Ocean

6. Bering Strait

7. 60°N, 149°W

8. Barrow

9. Juneau

10. northwest

Hawaii (Page 33)
Evaluate the Map

1. Hawaii

2. the extent of Hawaii and its major physical features

3. political boundaries, land and water features, key, scale, compass rose, lat. and long., individual towns and cities

4. 19°N, 22°N; 155°W, 160°W

5. 5/8":25 mi; 9 mm:25 km

6. answers will vary

7. answers will vary

8. Pacific Ocean

9. answers will vary

Activity Page
1. 3
2. northwest
3. southeast
4. Kaunakakai
5. ~250 mi, ~400 km
6. no
7. southeast
8. Lihue
9. 22°N, 159.5°W
10. state highway

Alberta (Page 35)
Evaluate the Map
1. Alberta
2. the extent of Alberta and its major physical features
3. political boundaries, land and water features, key, scale, compass rose, grid lines, individual towns or cities, information specific to the people
4. N/A
5. 9/16":50 mi; 9 mm:50 km
6. answers will vary
7. answers will vary
8. Lake Athabasca
9. answers will vary

Activity Page
1. that road is a Trans-Canada Highway
2. the sedimentary rock holds many dinosaur bones
3. the town of Peace River
4. Grande Prairie; It turns into Highway 2.
5. Trans-Canada 16, Provincial Highways 2, 44, and 28
6. Lac La Biche
7. ~125 mi, ~200 km
8. the town is south of the river
9. 4C
10. They should take Highway 58 E to 88 S to 2E. Where 2 meets 44,

they should stay on Highway 2, which will turn south.

Canada's Atlantic Coast (Page 37)
Evaluate the Map
1. Canada's Atlantic Coast
2. the extent of Canada's Atlantic Coast and its major physical features
3. political boundaries, land and water features, key, scale, compass rose, lat. and long., individual towns or cities, information specific to the people
4. 43°N, 54°N; 54°W, 70°W
5. 15/16":100 mi; 15 mm:100 km
6. answers will vary
7. answers will vary
8. Atlantic Ocean
9. answers will vary

Activity Page
1. Halifax
2. Fredericton
3. St. Pierre & Miquelon
4. north
5. St. Lawrence River
6. ~50 mi, ~80km
7. northeast
8. 4:00
9. 46°N, 64.5°W
10. St. John's

Yosemite National Park (Page 39)
Evaluate the Map
1. Yosemite National Park
2. Yosemite Valley National Park region, its convenience facilities, and its major physical features.
3. land and water features, key, scale, compass rose, information specific to the people
4. N/A
5. 3/4":0.25 mi; 12 mm:0.25 km

6. answers will vary
7. answers will vary
8. Merced River
9. answers will vary

Activity Page
1. dotted line trails are paved, dashed line trails are not
2. a ranger station, restrooms, picnic area, and parking
3. campgrounds
4. the Yosemite Museum and Indian Village, Ansel Adams gallery, Park Headquarters, Medical Clinic, and Village Store
5. Merced River
6. No, it is closed November to May
7. North Pines
8. cascades or falls
9. Four Mile Trail
10. the U.S. Court building

Chicago, Illinois (Page 41)
Evaluate the Map
1. Chicago, Illinois
2. the extent of Chicago, Illinois and its major political and physical features
3. political boundaries, land and water features, key, scale, compass rose, grid lines, individual towns or cities, information specific to the people
4. N/A
5. 3/8":2 mi; 6 mm:2 km
6. answers will vary
7. answers will vary
8. Lake Michigan
9. answers will vary

Activity Page
1. a
2. d
3. b
4. a
5. c

6. d

**Los Angeles,
California (Page 43)
Evaluate the Map**

1. Los Angeles, California

2. the extent of Los Angeles County, its surrounding areas, and its major physical features

3. political boundaries, land and water features, key, scale, compass rose, grid lines, individual towns or cities, information specific to the people

4. N/A

5. 3/4":4 mi; 12 mm:4 km

6. answers will vary

7. answers will vary

8. Pacific Ocean

9. answers will vary

Activity Page

1. c

2. d

3. b

4. a

5. b

6. a